MEET THE MASTER

POWER JADE FIRE

The next day, Hiro returns to the Dojo.

I am ready for more training!

There will be no training today, Hiro.

You must now learn about your enemy!

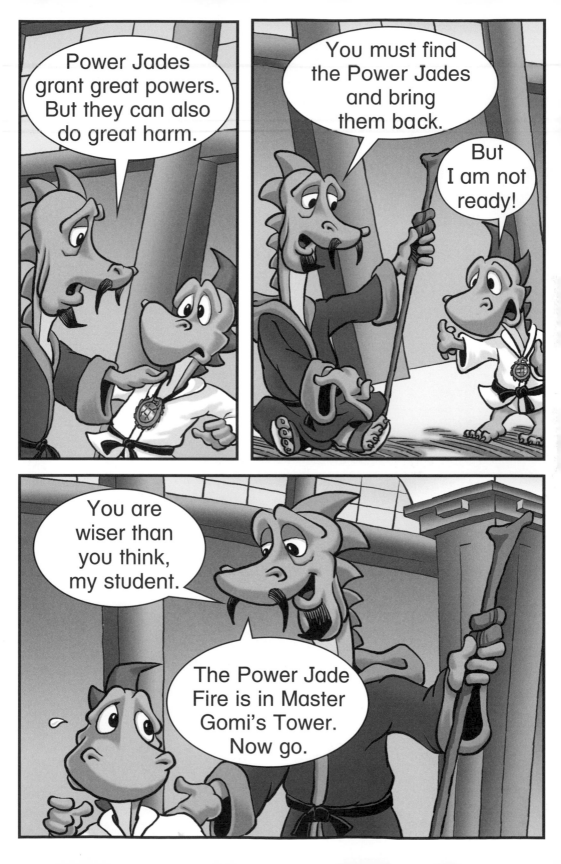

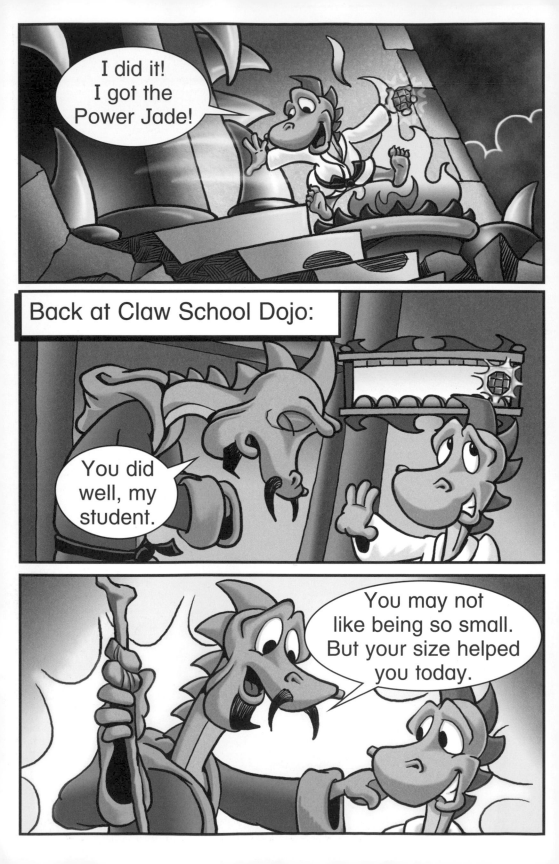

THE BIG FIGHT

Evil Master Gomi knows about Hiro now.

I will not let Master Fu win!

I will force all the dragons to help me take over the city!